Scott Foresman

Accelerating English Language Learning

Newcomer Book A

Authors
Anna Uhl Chamot
Jim Cummins
Carolyn Kessler
J. Michael O'Malley
Lily Wong Fillmore

Consultant
George González

Writers
Ellen Balla
Carolyn Grigsby

Longman

ISBN 0-13-027536-0
Copyright © 2001, 1997 Scott, Foresman and Company
All Rights Reserved. Printed in the United States of America.
This publication is protected by Copyright and permission should be obtained
from the publisher prior to any prohibited reproduction, storage in a retrieval
system, or transmission in any form or by any means, electronic, mechanical,
photocopying, recording, or otherwise. For information regarding permission,
write to:
Pearson Education
10 Bank Street, White Plains, NY 10606

3 4 5 6 7 8 9 10-WC-05 04 03 02 01

TABLE OF CONTENTS

TABLE OF CONTENTS

7 ## Lesson Seven • Working at School.................25
- to identify/say action verbs
- to practice the present-progressive tense
- to review classroom objects
- to talk/write about school activities
- to make connections

8 ## Lesson Eight • Lunchtime.....................29
- to identify/say foods
- to express preferences
- to identify/say meals
- to review time
- to survey classmates

9 ## Lesson Nine • After School....................33
- to identify/say action verbs
- to practice the present-progressive tense
- to express preferences
- to talk about after-school activities
- to survey classmates

10 ## Lesson Ten • My Neighborhood...............37
- to identify/say neighborhood places
- to review action verbs
- to practice the present-progressive tense
- to make connections
- to make a map

Tell what you know.

Look. Say.

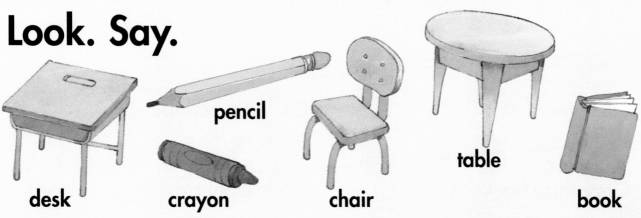

desk   pencil   crayon   chair   table   book

Look. Count. Write.

	zero	0
	one	1
	two	2
	three	3
	four	4
	five	5
	six	6
	seven	7
	eight	8
	nine	9
	ten	10

Count. Circle.

Circle two desks.

Circle six pencils.

Circle three books.

Circle eight crayons.

Write numbers. Play bingo.

Tell what you have.

page 41

Circle.

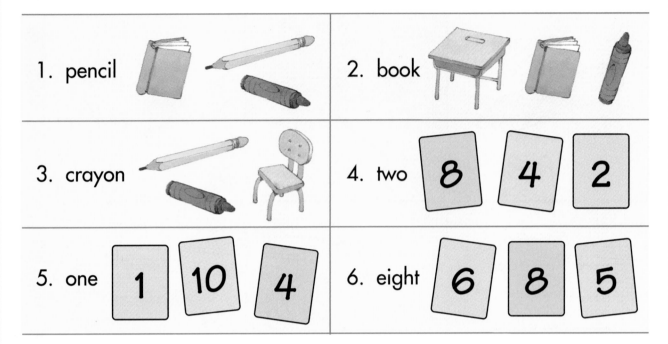

1. pencil

2. book

3. crayon

4. two   8   4   2

5. one   1   10   4

6. eight   6   8   5

Write the number.

I have 2 crayons. I have 1 book. What do you have?

I have _____ pencils.

I have _____ books.

I have _____ crayons.

2 About Me

Tell what you know.

Look. Say.

house

phone

phone number

address

street

Say the letters.

Aa Bb Cc Dd Ee Ff Gg Hh Ii
Jj Kk Ll Mm Nn Oo Pp Qq
Rr Ss Tt Uu Vv Ww Xx Yy Zz

Write. Say your phone number.

My phone number is

_____

_____ .

Hello?

Write your name. Spell it.

_____

My name is _____ .

Write a word you know.

Spell it.

b-o-o-k

_____

_____

Write the letters. Chant.

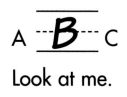

A ---B--- C

Look at me.

----- ----- E F -----

What do you see?

----- ----- -----

H ----- J -----

What do you say?

L ----- N -----

I say, " No!"

----- ----- -----

----- ----- R S ----- U V

The last four letters are

----- -----

----- ----- Y Z.

Make an address book. ✂ page 43

Write.

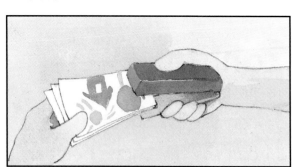

Draw.

Cut.

Staple.

Circle the word.

1.  house phone	2.  crayon pen	3.  phone number phone	4.  chair book

Write the letters.

a b ___ ___ d e f ___ ___ h i j ___ ___ l m ___

___ p q ___ s ___ u v w ___ y z

Write about yourself.

My name is _____ .

My phone number is _____ .

My address is _____ .

I can.

☐ I can say my address.

☐ I can say my phone number.

☐ I can say the alphabet.

Tell what you know.

Say the times.

It's twelve o'clock.

It's three o'clock.

It's six o'clock.

It's nine o'clock.

Say the colors.

red   orange   yellow   green   blue   purple

Say the shapes.

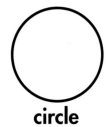 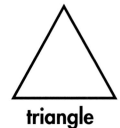 

circle   triangle   square

Color the shapes.

1. Color the circle red.
2. Color the triangle blue.
3. Color the square orange.

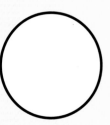 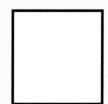 

Match. Say the times.

 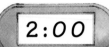 

2:00

12:00

3:00

1:00

1.

 2.

3.

Draw a picture.

Use circles, squares, and triangles.

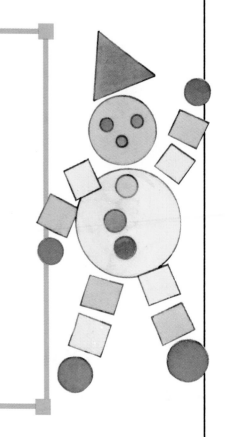

Make the clock. page 45

Say the rhyme.

Hello. Hello. What do you say?
I'm Mr. Clock. It's time to play.

I say "tick tock." I say "tick tock."
What time is it? Look at the clock.

It's time to go. Good-by! Tick tock.
What time is it? It's 10:00.

Match the times.

1.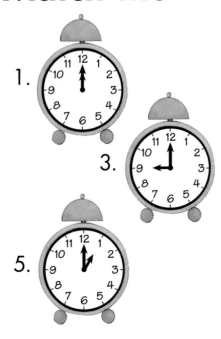

3.

5.

11:00

9:00

1:00

12:00

6:00

10:00

2.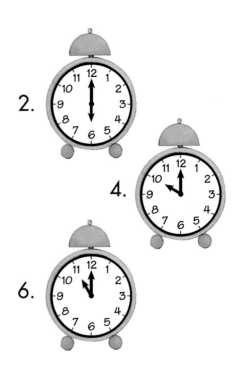

4.

6.

Tell about you.

Draw hands on the clocks.

1. What time do you go to school?

2. What time do you go home?

I can. ✔

☐ I can tell time.

☐ I can say ◯ ▢ △ .

☐ I can say ● ● ● ● ● ● .

Tell what you know.

Say the days.

Sunday	Monday	Tuesday	Wednesday	Thursday	Friday	Saturday
1	2	3	4	5	6	7

Count.

11 eleven	**12** twelve	**13** thirteen	**14** fourteen	**15** fifteen	**16** sixteen

17 seventeen	**18** eighteen	**19** nineteen	**20** twenty	**21** twenty-one

Look at the pictures. Say.

1.

2.

3.

Circle the word.

1.

art   music   library

2.

library   music   art

Say the chant.
Write your birthday month.

January, February, March, April, May
These are the months. There are more to say.

June, July, August, and September,
Next comes October, November, and December.

Look at the months. How many can you say?
Look at the calendar. When is your birthday?

My birthday is in _____ .

My birthday
is in June.

January
February
March
April
May
June
July
August
September
October
November
December

Make a calendar. page 47

Cut.

Paste.

Draw.

Write.

Circle the number.

1. eleven	12	15	14	11	2. twenty-one	18	20	21	13
3. thirteen	13	15	11	16	4. fifteen	17	20	15	11

Circle the word.

1.

art   music   library

2.

library   music   art

What's today? Circle.

Sunday   Monday   Tuesday   Wednesday

Thursday   Friday   Saturday

I can.

- ☐ I can count to 21.
- ☐ I can say the days of the week.
- ☐ I can say the months of the year.
- ☐ I can say **music   art   library**.

5 ▼ My School

Tell what you know.

I'm Mrs. Cook. I'm a teacher.

classroom

I'm Mrs. Smith. I'm the nurse.

School Nurse

nurse's office

I'm Mrs. Jackson. I'm the principal.

office

I'm Mr. Gonzalez. I'm the librarian.

library

rest room

What time is it? Say the times.

It's nine thirty.

10:30

It's ten thirty.

It's one thirty.

3:30

It's three thirty.

Who is this? Say the words.

principal   nurse   teacher   librarian

Draw the times.

1.

2.

3.

4.

Match. Circle.

1.

2.

3.

Read the story.

I'm **Adam**. This is my **school**. 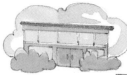 I go to

school at **8:30**. My favorite class is **music**.

I go to music at **9:30**. This is my **music teacher**.

At **3:30** I go **home**.

Write about you.

1. I go to school  at

2. I go to English class  at

3. I go home at

Make a book about you. page 49

Cut.

Draw and write.

Staple.

Draw the times.

1.  **11:30**

2.  **9:30**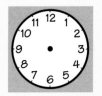

3.  **4:30**

4.  **1:30**

Draw a line. Name.

1.

2.

3.

a.

b.

c.

I can.

☐ I can tell time.

☐ I can talk about my school.

Tell what you know.

What are you wearing today?

I'm wearing shorts.

What are you wearing today?

I'm wearing a raincoat.

Look. Say.

pants

T-shirt

raincoat

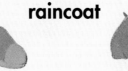
jacket

shorts

shoes

umbrella

dress

Say the weather.

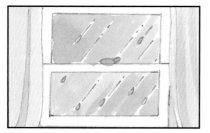
It's rainy.

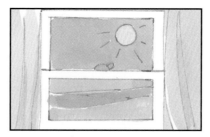
It's sunny.

It's snowy.

Match.

It's snowy.

It's rainy.

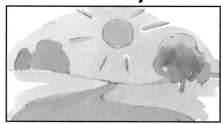
It's sunny.

umbrella

raincoat

hat

T-shirt

jacket

shorts

Circle the word.

1.
pants
jacket

2.
hat
T-shirt

3.
shorts
dress

Read the story.

Hi. I'm **Chris**. I'm wearing a **red T-shirt**. I'm wearing

brown pants. I'm wearing **green shoes**. I have

a **blue backpack**.

Practice with a partner.

Write a story. Draw.

Hi! My name is _____.

I'm wearing _____.

I'm wearing _____.

I have _____.

Make a picture. page 51

Cut.

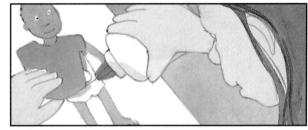

Glue.

Draw the clothes.

blue pants

red T-shirt

Circle the weather.

It's sunny.   It's rainy.

It's rainy.   It's snowy.

I can.

☐ I can say the names of clothing.

☐ I can say the weather.

☐ I can talk about my clothes.

Tell what you know.

What are you doing?

I'm working on the computer.

Look. Say.

adding

measuring

painting

working on the computer

reading

writing

Say the words.

subtracting

drawing

kicking the ball

playing soccer

singing

running

Draw. Say the words.

What are you doing?

1.

2.

3.

I'm adding.

I'm painting.

I'm reading.

Practice with a partner.

What are you doing?

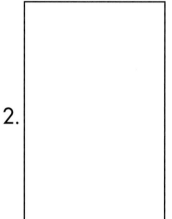
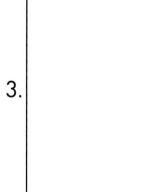

I'm writing a story.

Match.

Act it out. ✂ page 53

Take a card.

Act it out.

Have a partner guess.

Read the story.

It's Tuesday. I'm writing a story.

Now I'm adding.

Now it's recess. I'm jumping rope.

Now I'm reading a book.

Circle the word.

1.

painting

reading

2.

kicking

writing

Write the words.

1.

_____

I'm _____ .

2.

_____

I'm _____ .

I can.

☐ I can write about what I do at school.

☐ I can talk about what I do at school.

Tell what you know.

What do you like?

I like apples.

Look. Say.

apples

bananas

juice

sandwiches

milk

pizza

cookies

Say the words.

corn

chicken

broccoli

ice cream

rice

bread

Draw. Say the words.

What do you like?

I like _____ .

I like _____ .

I like _____ .

I like _____ .

Ask your friends.

Name	Likes
Luisa	pizza
1.	
2.	
3.	

Read the story.

For breakfast, I like to eat cereal.

For lunch, I like to eat a sandwich.

For dinner, I like to eat chicken.

Draw and write.

1. For breakfast, I like to eat _____ .

2. For lunch, I like to eat _____ .

3. For dinner, I like to eat _____ .

Make a meal. page 55

Cut.

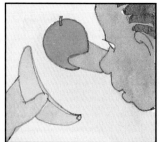
Choose.

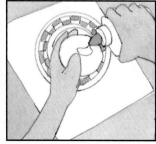
Glue.

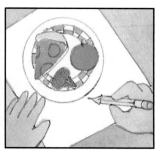
Write.

Draw the food.

1. [ ]

apple

2. [ ]

sandwiches

Write the words.

1.

_____

2.

_____

pizza

milk

Circle the meal.

1.

breakfast
lunch
dinner

2.

breakfast
lunch
dinner

3.

breakfast
lunch
dinner

I can. ✔

☐ I can say the names of food.

☐ I can say what I like.

☐ I can ask my friends what they like.

Tell what you know.

Look. Say.

read a book   **ride my bike**   **jump rope**   **go to the library**

Practice with a partner.

Ask your friends.

Name	Likes to
Jamal	read

Draw and write.

What do you like to do?

I like to

_____

- -

_____

_____

- -

_____ .

Read the sentences.

He's doing his homework.

She's reading a book.

Circle the sentence.

What are they doing?

1.

He's riding a bike.

He's playing soccer.

2.

She's reading a book.

She's playing the piano.

3.

He's eating a snack.

He's doing his homework.

Make a book. page 57

Write.

Cut.

Staple.

Read it aloud.

Draw.

1. 2.

He's reading a book. **She's eating a snack.**

Write. Use the words in the box.

What do they like to do?

read a book
play the piano

1.

I like to ______________________.

2.

I like to ______________________.

I can.

☐ I can talk about what I do after school.

☐ I can write about what I do after school.

☐ I can ask my friends what they do after school.

Tell what you know.

Say the words.

library

post office

supermarket

school

park

mall

Say the words.

bus stop   **fire station**   **police station**   **laundromat**

Practice with a partner.

Where are you going?

To the park.

Circle the word.

1.

park

post office

2.

supermarket

park

3.

library

post office

Match.

I'm checking out a book.

I'm mailing a letter.

We're washing clothes.

We're buying food.

Make a map. page 59

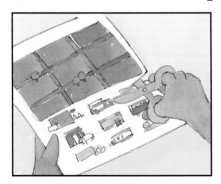

Cut.

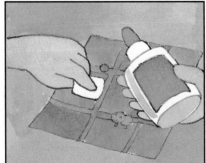

Glue.

Share.

Write. Use the words in the box.

1.

_____

_____

2.

_____

_____

3.

_____

_____

Circle the sentence.

Where are they?

They're at the laundromat.
They're at the post office.

He's at the library.
He's at the park.

They're at the bus stop.
They're at the supermarket.

She's at the post office.
She's at the library.

I can. ✔

☐ I can talk about places in my neighborhood.

☐ I can write about places in my neighborhood.

☐ I can make a map.

Cut.

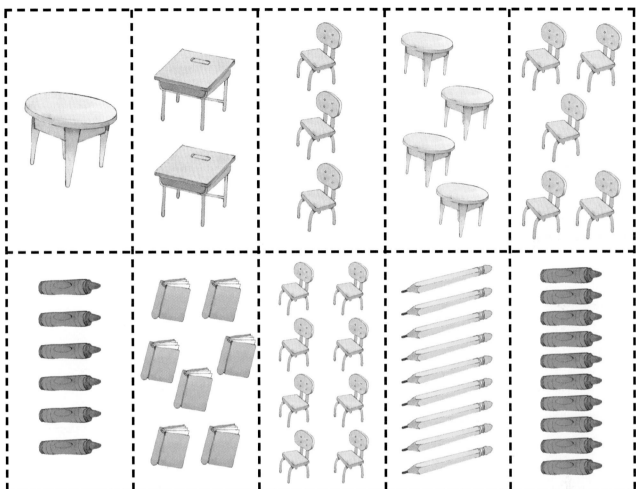

Make a name tag.

My name is

Cut.

1

8

My name is

_____

- - - - - - - - - - - - - -

_____

_____

- - - - - - - - - - - - - -

_____

2

3

My phone number is

_____

- - - - - - - - - - - - - -

_____

4

5

My address is

_____

- - - - - - - - - - - - - -

_____

_____

- - - - - - - - - - - - - -

_____

6

7

Cut out the shapes.

Cut. Write your classes.

1	paste		Wednesday
2	paste		Friday
3	paste		Sunday
4	paste		Tuesday
5	paste		Thursday
6	paste		Saturday
7	paste		Monday

Cut out the pages.

All About Me

I'm _____

_____ .

This is my house.

This is my teacher.

This is my principal.

This is my classroom.

Cut. Make a picture.

Cut out the cards. Act them out.

running

adding
4 + 5 = 9

subtracting
7 −2 5

singing

working on the computer
cactus

writing
Today is Tue

eating

measuring

kicking the ball

painting

jumping rope

reading
OUT IN SPACE

Cut. Make a meal.

Cut. Make a book.

What Are They Doing?

by

_____
- - - - - - - - - - - - - - - - - - - -
_____
- - - - - - - - - - - - - - - - - - - -
_____

_____
- - - - - - - - - - - - - - - - - - - -
She's _____.

_____
- - - - - - - - - - - - - - - - - - - -
They're _____.

_____
- - - - - - - - - - - - - - - - - - - -
He's _____.

_____
- - - - - - - - - - - - - - - - - - - -
She's _____.

_____
- - - - - - - - - - - - - - - - - - - -
He's _____.

Cut. Make a map.

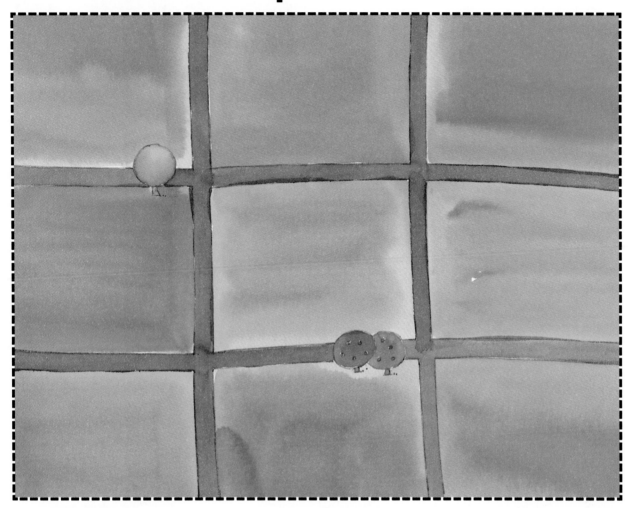

Illustrations by Elizabeth Allen